# Eden: the second book
## watch us grow

**eden project**

# Contents

Published 2002 by Eden Project Books
a division of Transworld Publishers

ISBN 1-903-91-912-6
Design © the Eden Project/
Transworld Publishers

Text by Martin Jackson
Design by Gendall Design, Cornwall
Printed in Cornwall by St Ives Roche Ltd

The Eden Project
Bodelva, St Austell, Cornwall PL24 2SG
www.edenproject.com

The Eden Trust: Registered Charity No. 1052127

Transworld Publishers
61-63 Uxbridge Road, London W5 5SA
a division of the Random House Group
www.booksattransworld.co.uk

A Millennium Commission
Lottery Project

eden project books

# Introduction
## Tony Kendle, Foundation Director

Our gardens and displays are about plants, but we use those plants as a lens to focus in on the amazing worlds that each one represents, how the politics of the world lie within a cup of sweet tea. Our plants were chosen because they could tell a story, and every story is there – gruesome, awesome, funny or inspirational. They tell of amazing science, giving us hope for food security, clean technologies and improved health. They tell of how each one of us, already, is a global citizen. We have created wonders to see here in Cornwall, but of course they are just echoes of the real world's diversity, and our stories of them are echoes of the real lives that people live in these places. How can we do justice to these lives?

We have tried by first creating the best setting we could. You will notice our 'two decent greenhouses'. The structures are remarkable masterpieces of efficiency in design and engineering, pointing towards one solution to reducing resource consumption. They have a cathedral quality. They are a fitting stage for some of the greatest stories ever told. They give us room to evoke a sense of the grandeur of the landscapes we are talking about. Already, you are able to stand and feel something of the majesty of the rainforest giants. You will be able to close your eyes and catch the scents of the wild Mediterranean or the Spice Islands.

Eden is built within a pit used for china clay extraction. This is an old industry that has shaped the economy and also the very landscape of

Cornwall, but today massive change is underway. Eden stands at the gateway of a region being reshaped for a positive future.

You can learn more about this in our exhibits. For the time being, though, just stand by the side of this green oasis and think about what lies underneath. Our garden grows in sterile wastes that have not felt the warmth of sunlight for millions of years. In some areas we are working on pure sand, in others on relentless clay, with slopes and gradients that would make a goat think twice, let alone our horticultural staff. We have undertaken one of the most ambitious soil-creation projects ever seen, manufacturing a range of different soils for different needs, using all recycled wastes and of course avoiding peat.

Why did we give ourselves such a challenge? We did it partly for the drama appropriate to the stories we want to tell, and partly to be good neighbours and not affect the skyline. Most of all, however, we wanted Eden to be a symbol of what is possible when people put their mind to the challenge of regeneration and restoration. It is working well, but we hope not so well that the origins and challenges of the pit ever become invisible.

Spare a thought then for our horticultural team. Not only do they have to grow plants from every corner of the world under the most challenging conditions, but no one has ever had to fly a greenhouse of that size before.

This is their story...

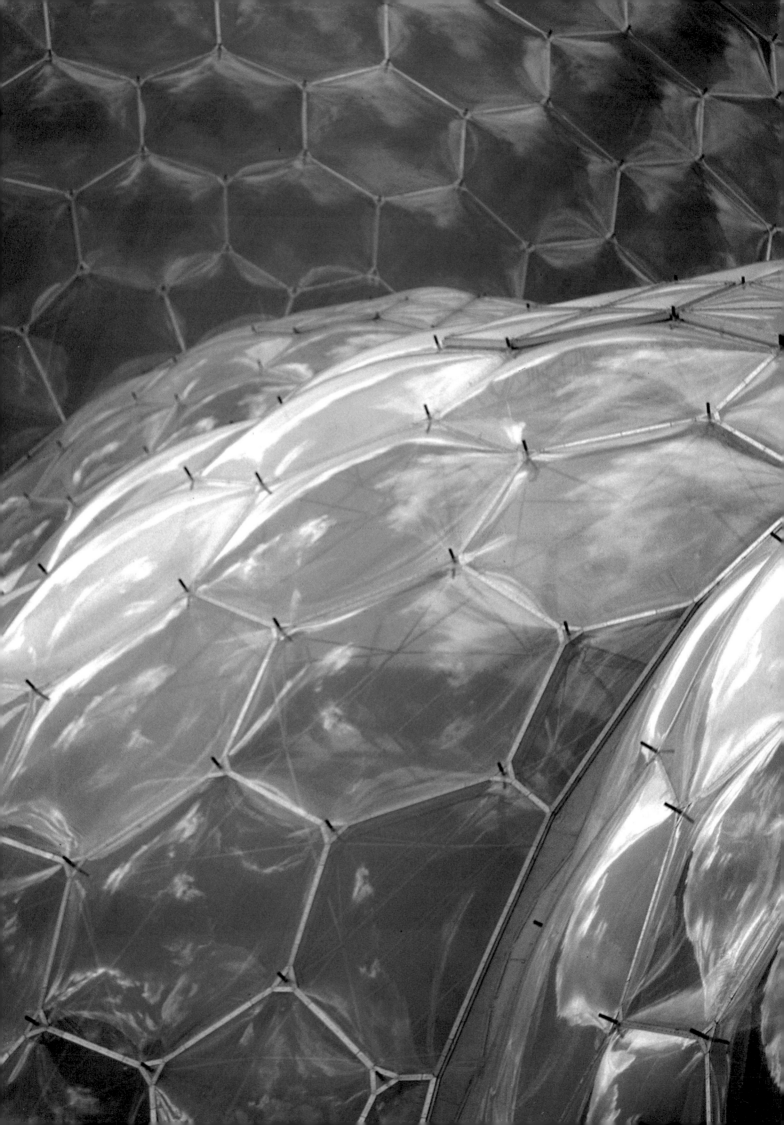

# Today
## the Llawnroc Inn
# tomorrow the world

Most of the attention that Eden has attracted so far has naturally focused on the biomes – and mighty fine biomes they are. The brief for designers and constructors was to come up with buildings of sufficient architectural merit to match the world's great iconic structures such as the Sydney Opera House.

They also had to be buildings fit for a function: to contain plants from an extraordinary range of habitats and to protect them. It was a tremendous task, achieved with style, drama and amazing grace, as the awed reaction of thousands of visitors seeing them in this setting for the first time demonstrates.

Tim Smit and Philip McMillan Browse, then Horticultural Director at Heligan, later to do the same job at Eden, first began to kick the idea around just seven years ago over a few drinks at the Llawnroc Inn in Gorran Haven. They were trying to think of something that would bring more people to Cornwall, particularly those who would be interested in visiting gardens. A host of ideas were rejected because they weren't big enough; Tim and Philip knew that if it was going to be effective, it had to be of a different order, a different scale.

6

So someone said, let's build the biggest greenhouse in the world. At the time television screens were full of stories of the Amazon being cut down and burnt. So, they thought, why not put a tropical rainforest in it?

Both Tim and Philip were acutely aware that the runaway success of Heligan owed most to a great curiosity about the way its Victorian owners had worked with plants for their own ends, and in particular to visitors' fascination with the renovated productive gardens. That led them to the decision to create a new type of botanical garden for the twenty-first century. It would focus on mankind's relationship with plants, and therefore land use. They would tell the whole story, from wild plants and their conservation to how man has manipulated all those wild plants to create the crops we depend on today.

Peter Thoday, a Heligan trustee recently retired as Head of Horticulture at Bath University, was brought on board as Co-Director of Horticulture. Together Philip and Peter roughed out plant lists and sketched in the concept, pulling together similar climatic regions in different parts of the world and dealing with issues of conservation and agronomy – very different from most botanic gardens.

The aim was to reveal the many ways in which people everywhere have tackled the same challenge – the common achievements, costs, and potential remedies – and, like a spark arcing into a box of fireworks, illuminating all this with an explosive charge of science and showmanship.

As Philip and Peter discovered when they rifled through their address books, seeking the expertise they needed to put flesh on the bones of the idea, they never had any difficulty in inspiring other people to think that the idea was worthwhile. The defining moment came in July 1996; a meeting in Bristol organized by Peter Thoday and attended by around twenty of the country's leading young minds from relevant areas of science and botany.

Between them the group knew most of what there was to know about greenhouse growing, landscape project management, light transmission through glass and foil, biological control of pests, plant genetic resources, environmental science ... They all threw in their sixpenny-worth on their specialist subjects, but they also understood the realm of possibility. When they walked in through the door, a tribe of ideas marched in with them.

Philip still finds it amazing when he looks back. The project was no more than a dream at that stage, yet these people freely gave their time and thought to determining what the philosophy and policy would be. They knew that what was needed was not another conventional scientific organization with people in white coats scurrying between laboratories, but rather a science communication

# They all threw in their sixpenny-worth on their specialist subjects, but they also understood the realm of possibility. When they walked in through the door, a tribe of ideas marched in with them.

centre. It would complement existing expertise, champion and cooperate with it. Rather than compete for the same ever-declining pot of money, it would aim to build public and political awareness of why the issues were important.

Of course staff were needed, to pick up the ideas and run. One of the biggest problems with an enterprise like this, Philip says, is that people like himself can have the vision, but experience also creates constraints that don't always allow you to see how the thing might develop. 'My experience would tell me that something can't be done – but if you ask people who don't know it can't be done, they find a way to do it. Our founding staff were young, intellectually very capable, very enthusiastic, and enormously committed – they joined in the days when we had no idea whether the project would succeed, and it couldn't have been done without them.'

# The Plant Hunters I:
# Buddy,
## can you spare a lime?

The plant exhibits at Eden lift the lid on a whole world of research, economics, politics and more. But even before the foundations for the biomes were laid the plants which would star in these stories had to be found and raised.

**Above:** Ian Martin.

8

In 1997 the Watering Lane nursery at Pentewan was bought and extended to provide a temporary home, and during the first few weeks in the nursery the Green Team, and in particular nursery manager Ian Martin, weren't so much trying to find plants as cope with the supply. Botanical gardens and universities were offering everything from a few cuttings to the entire contents of redundant hothouses. This was a brilliant start for the collection, and all gratefully received – but it was also an alarming reminder of the decline both in interest in horticultural careers and in research investment, a state of affairs which Eden aims to address.

Within a fortnight there was a call from Cannington Countryside College to say that they were shutting down their stove-house. 'If we wanted anything we were to dig it up and take it away,' says Philip McMillan Browse. 'There was masses of stuff. You'll see a lot of yellow orchids in the Humid Tropics Biome – they came from an armful there that had grown and grown untended for three years.' This sort of thing happened repeatedly. The Team were suddenly showered with material, even before they knew exactly what they wanted, how many, or what they were going to do with them.

The Green Team researched, read, applied their own knowledge – Robin Lock, for instance, brought many years' experience as a

There were
field trips to
Cameroon,
the Seychelles,
Malaysia
and Guyana.

tropical forester to his role as Curator of the Humid Tropics Biome – and picked others' brains, to work up a palette of 'useful' plants that would provide natural and realistic displays for each of the regions to be represented in the three biomes.

To begin with, procurement was easy. Many of the research centres and institutes developing tropical crops are based in Europe – partly to provide a buffer against the international spread of pests and disease, which could occur if these plants were transferred straight from one growing region to another. From these came dozens of cultivated varieties of banana, rice, rubber trees, coffee, coconut palms, cocoa. Today, with the biomes full and growing rapidly, there is no more room for donations but in the early days those gifts were priceless.

Plants from places like the Mediterranean are simple, but when it comes to others, such as West Africa, where perhaps only a handful of species are commercially available, where do you even start to source the range of plants required? The answer is to commission people to go out and collect seed for you. This couldn't all be done by simply sitting on the phone, either. There were field trips to Cameroon, the Seychelles, Malaysia and Guyana. Contact had already been made with organizations in these areas; Eden is about plants and people, after all, and it was important to meet them to ensure that they were honestly represented.

Although this was all relatively straightforward, it wouldn't have happened if the team had been unable to convince donors that Eden was a serious scientific enterprise in the making.

Tom Keay, Curator of the Warm Temperate Biome, says, 'That was critical in winning all this co-operation. There is a debt there that we must repay by promoting donor organizations like IRRI [the International Rice Research Institute], and explaining to people what they do.' Robin Lock also organized longer-term research projects in the countries visited. He drew up guidelines and questionnaires for each subject, and local students compiled a wealth of data and sent it all back to him. For instance, in Malaysia they visited home garden owners and talked to them about their lives, the size of their plots, everything they grew and why.

'It was one of the simplest and most effective of the projects,' says Robin. 'With that information we could create an honest picture of what a typical home garden in Sabah looked like – which plants were cash crops, which of those sold best, which they grew for themselves, the balance between the two. There was a huge amount of really interesting detail coming directly from Malaysian people themselves.'

**Left:** Walkways in Malaysia.
**Below:** Coco de Mer palms growing wild in the Seychelles.
**Bottom left:** The common coconut growing in a plantation.
**Bottom centre:** Inga, an Amazonian forest tree.
**Bottom right:** Bananas in the greenhouse at Watering Lane.

A vital delivery came from Central America. The team was keen to track down species of Inga, an important group of Amazonian forest trees. The problem was that the seeds germinate in just four days. They contacted a scientist from the Royal Botanical Gardens at Kew, who was working with the plants in Honduras. The day he came home he picked some seeds, brought them back to London, and they were transported down to Eden overnight. Forty-eight hours later, they were sprouting in their pots.

There were other sources, closer to home, but equally unconventional.

A member of the team went off to Brixton market in London and scoured the stalls for boxes of yams and ginger. 'We wanted loads of ginger around the edge of the Humid Tropics Biome where the heating is, because they're very hardy in that sense. They had to be commercial varieties to demonstrate production techniques, so that was the obvious place to get them,' Philip points out.

Gradually lists were crossed out. Seeds arrived in the post; propagated plants packed the nursery. But trees were needed that were big enough to make people feel small – to create the sense of a rainforest canopy in the Humid Tropics Biome from day one. There was no time to grow them – but no need to, anyway. The plant-hunting business has come a long way since intrepid explorers nurtured seedlings of new species through long months at sea; these days it's done by remote control.

The job was contracted out to a specialist grower in Holland, who tours nurseries worldwide to find mature trees for interior decorators dressing the atria of swanky hotels and shopping malls. He was given a list of requirements, and when he was off in Florida or wherever, and saw something, he took a picture with a digital camera and downloaded it to computer at Watering Lane.

If Eden wanted the tree he bought it and transported it to Holland, potted it up in quarantine, and grew it on for delivery when it was needed for the biome.

11

# The Plant Hunters II:
# gum-tree
# gumshoe

There was no point in plonking all these plants down and just saying they were all useful, for whatever reason. So the palette of 4,000-odd species has been woven into more than eighty major exhibits. Between them they explain the stories of mono-cultures and diversity, of feast and famine, fair trade and greed, politics and religion, land use and abuse, wild and tamed, history and future – the full spectrum of Eden's curiosity.

In this area particularly the wow-factor has to be matched where necessary with the greatest possible degree of authenticity. Otherwise it would be like one of those wooden Hollywood movies where you suddenly notice an extra in the big Viking fight scene wearing a watch. It is important – and more intriguing for visitors – to go that extra mile for accuracy.

Dr Andrew Ormerod, Eden's specialist in cultivated plants, has circled the globe many times by phone, fax and e-mail, digging out the detail on what we should use and how. On a typical day he might call the Bronx Botanical Garden in New York for a specimen of a scarce day-lily dating from the 1930s, write to growers in France about the rare rose cultivar 'Rose de Mai', chat to an archaeo-botanist about brewing in Ancient Egypt, and gratefully accept the

offer of a teasel machine, once used in the wool trade, from a museum in Lancashire for eventual display.

It has been a big job. Some exhibits, like the sugar cane and oil palm, are just single varieties. But the average is about ten varieties per exhibit – around 800 specific plants to find. A Bacchanalian theme had been chosen for our Vines exhibit, and we needed the oldest varieties we could get. Andrew set off to track down obscure examples: the 'Muscat of Alexandria' cultivar, which goes back maybe 2,000 years; "Malvasia", source of the butt of malmsey said to have been the death of the Duke of Clarence in 1478; 'Viogonier', a wine variety that had almost vanished, but that according to connoisseurs is set for a big comeback; and 'Black Corinth', an old currant grape.

We have to be careful to check that suppliers have permits to trade in these obscure species, or that the material comes from legitimate environmental projects.

'The "Black Corinth" was actually very difficult to find,' says Andrew. 'Very often you can acquire these things by ringing around growers, nursery owners and gardeners in the areas where they were most often grown – and those people have been incredibly helpful. That's how we got the "Viogonier", through some contacts in France. But the "Black Corinth" eventually came from quite an unexpected source, an amateur collector in Belgium.'

Sometimes Andrew has been able to locate particular plants but has been unable to get his hands on them – for very good reason. *Barlia robertiana* is a Mediterranean orchid exploited as a source of 'salep', a starch used in the Turkish ice-cream trade. It has been so plundered in the wild that it is now protected under international CITES regulations governing the export of endangered species.

The only reason for growing the orchid at Eden would be to flag up the conservation story. We might strike lucky in the future and obtain it from a botanical garden – but obviously if it came here from its natural home that would send entirely the wrong message. We have to be careful to check that suppliers have permits

When it was analysed against archaeological records, we found it also contained the seeds of a weed associated with the very beginnings of cultivation – which for our purposes was brilliant.

to trade in these obscure species, or that the material comes from legitimate environmental projects. There are also restrictions to prevent the spread of potentially devastating plant diseases. Bringing in grape-seed or vines from outside Europe, for instance, is a complete no-no.

Sometimes Andrew has been completely stumped, as with the so-far fruitless search for specimens of the *Boswellia* and *Commiphora* aromatic gum resin trees that produce frankincense and myrrh. So if anybody out there is preparing a slavishly accurate nativity play, please get in touch.

Usually, dogged determination has worked. Sniffing out plants for the Perfume exhibit, Andrew really wanted the legendary Jasmine cultivar, 'Jasmine de Grasse', which provides one of the most expensive scent ingredients in the world. The chances of obtaining it were slim – cultivation had declined to a mere hectare in its native Provence. But then, through a chance remark, he found one – in a nursery just up the road in Devon.

During a trip to Spain to collect sub-tropical trees and Mediterranean wild plant seed from a WWF nursery, he followed up a tip-off from a Spanish scientist and headed for a village in the hills behind Malaga.

'She had told me that they were still growing Einkorn – an ancient cereal, one of the original crops from the Fertile Crescent,' says Andrew. 'We knew it had hung on in a few isolated mountain areas in Turkey, Morocco and Spain. When I got there, I discovered that they had stopped growing it just two years before, and I thought I was out of luck. Then an elderly man led me into his mule shed, pulled out a bag – and produced a handful of the last crop of his seeds.

'So we caught that in the nick of time. When it was analysed against archaeological records, we found it also contained the seeds of a weed associated with the very beginnings of cultivation – which for our purposes was brilliant.'

In a nearby architectural salvage centre, he also picked up old local tools to display with the exhibit – wooden threshing implements similar to those used by the Sumerians 5,000 years ago. Exploring those origins of agriculture has taken him down all sorts of arcane avenues of archaeology and ethno-botany, towards fundamental questions. How did our ancestors work out which plants were safe to eat? Was it by using some kind of primitive parlour game, where the tribe sat round distributing different bits to each other and waiting for a reaction; laughing uproariously if it occurred, then heading off to hunt for that universal plant medicine, the cure for diarrhoea? Possibly. It is known that during tribal disputes in some parts of the world a captive would be used as a guinea pig for early product testing. He'd be given the plant roasted, then boiled, and then raw; if he survived every stage, it would be put on the menu.

'Under even the simplest of questions there is great depth,' says Andrew. 'Sharing knowledge about these things at Eden will be a bit like an iceberg; in the exhibits we are showing a small amount presented simply. In the long term, we are building that great depth underneath; if people want to know more it will be available, and if they want even more than that, we'll have contacts they can then go to.'

It is known that during tribal disputes in some parts of the world a captive would be used as a guinea pig for early product testing.

# The Plant Hunters III:
# Data
## Protection Acts

Plant Records Manager Louise Frost oversees a rank of hefty fridges and freezers. **Not for pasty storage** – these are botanical bank vaults. They contain more than 3,500 packets of seed (the number grows daily), all carefully labelled detailing species, type, and provenance – where they originally came from, when, and how they arrived.

They're also logged into Eden's computer database – along with every cutting and plant brought here, or germinated and propagated in-house. Each specimen is bagged or tagged with name, rank and number translated into a bar code which follows them throughout their lives. (The people looking after these plants in the nursery care deeply for them, incidentally. Nothing is listed as 'dead' in the database – it is 'removed'.)

Altogether there have been some 11,500 'accessions', which could each be one plant, 100 seedlings or 1,000 seeds. These accessions continue to arrive by the hundreds every week, and have to be processed pretty much immediately before they get muddled up. It is Louise's job to count them all in, and count them all out again into the pit. Along the way – with the help of the Green Team who keep her bang up-to-date with information – she has created what is recognized in the field as the best-kept set of plant records in the country.

Louise acknowledges that she had an advantage – other botanical gardens are labouring with the legacy of often-incomplete plant accounting written in dusty ledgers dating back a century or more. She was able to make immediate use of highly sophisticated software. It has more than 200 cross-referencing tables, providing an exhaustive profile of each plant: source, Latin and common names, age, date of arrival, the medium used for propagation, current location in the nursery, growth rate, when it flowered, star sign, favourite song ... Well, maybe not, but it is extremely comprehensive.

The importance of this sort of detail becomes clearer when you take the example of the Chilean Forest exhibit on the outer rim of the pit – one of our long-term conservation projects. *Araucaria araucana*, (left) better known as the monkey puzzle tree, is seriously endangered in its native home. It is slowly dying out, due mainly to mass logging and the use of the seeds for fodder and human consumption. A team from Edinburgh Botanical Gardens collected seeds from different trees in the

'From a scientific point of view, that's something we really want to develop. We already have 64 different cultivars of rice. We're growing 44 different varieties of peppers.'

wild, employing global location satellite equipment so precise that by following the co-ordinates you could walk straight up to each parent tree in the forest at any time in the future – provided it is still there. The seeds were brought back to Edinburgh, germinated, and grown into seedlings. In May 1999 161 of these specimens were handed over to Eden to nurture and raise.

All the information gathered on their origin has been filed here, to be added to as their future health and development is monitored. Eventually these trees will provide a gene pool for the whole forest, away from its threatened environment, should it become extinct in the wild.

Louise actually finds the sheer number of plants she's handling less impressive than the range of diversity within species represented at Eden. 'From a scientific point of view, that's something we really want to develop. We already have 64 different cultivars of rice in our seed

Eventually these trees will provide a gene pool for DNA analysis, which will perhaps give some indication of what is going wrong back there in Chile.

store. We've grown 44 different types of pepper at our nursery. Almost by accident we've procured lots of different types of *Inga* tree species from Kew, after a researcher finished his work and needed a home for them. We now probably have the greatest number in the country.'

23

# Dirty stories

One of the great achievements at Eden could easily be overlooked, because it is right underfoot. While all the work of finding and processing plants was going on, somebody had to be sorting out stuff to grow them in. The pit was completely barren. Ordinary topsoil – even if enough could have been trucked in – wouldn't have been right for the job. So Eden made its own – 13,000 cubic metres of it, 80,000 tonnes.

It was a typically instant Eden decision. A challenge had to be met, and almost overnight, without any specific budget, one of the largest soil-manufacturing projects ever seen in this country set to, creating bespoke soil types that have never been made before, for purposes which have never been attempted before. This earth factory was only feasible because the necessary raw materials were to hand: sand waste from the local china clay industry, spoil from ball-clay workings in Devon, and organic waste – a mix of bark from the timber trade and domestic garden refuse.

Using these ingredients scientists at the University of Reading worked out a range of recipes suitable for all the plants at Eden, which

# The turf in the amphitheatre, for example, is growing in a particularly compaction-resistant blend capable of bearing the tramp of thousands of feet.

between them have radically different needs. The turf in the amphitheatre, for example, is growing in a particularly compaction-resistant blend capable of bearing the tramp of thousands of feet. The Humid Tropics Biome needed a high-performance mix. Juliet Rose, landscape restoration specialist, explains: 'You've got very high temperatures and humidity in there, so organic material in the soil breaks down very fast, and can quickly turn to dust. You can't prevent that happening, but we've tried to design a soil that will have the longest possible life.'

The Warm Temperate Biome presented its own set of tricky challenges, particularly in the South African and Mediterranean zones. Plants from the Fynbos region of South Africa, such as Protea (left) are incredibly sensitive to nutrients in the soil – too much is

# The ambition of the design team was to create something that looked, felt and smelled like the Mediterranean, where these plants are highly stressed by their growing conditions.

dangerously toxic. This soil had to be completely infertile.

The Mediterranean area required what was, in essence, a paradox. Juliet explains: 'The ambition of the design team was to create something that looked, felt and smelled like the Mediterranean, where these plants are highly stressed by their growing conditions. So we have had to do something which is probably unique – make a soil that gives the plants we want to grow a really hard time, but still keeps them alive.'

These different soil mixes all went through extensive trials in the nursery, but the real test was how they would work in the biomes. Tom Keay says, 'It was a big concern because it is such an experimental approach, but I think it is exactly what's required. Agricultural topsoil would have been disastrous – it would have given us huge, lush growth, which is precisely what we didn't want in there. Instead we have a neutral base material, low in nutrients and very free-draining – just right.'

Beyond the immediate growing needs, the soil project will underpin a rich seam of research programmes at Eden in the future – and perhaps a potential new industry for the South West, capable of turning eyesores into an environmentally sound product. The expertise is there – and there is no shortage of raw materials.

27

# Pest busters

If anybody at Eden needed reminding that you cannot take anything for granted, then they received a rude wake-up call with the arrival at the nursery of some of the big plants bought in to dress the biomes for opening. **They brought with them some uninvited guests, which could be real party-poopers in the biomes themselves, even if they presented no threat to Cornwall at large because they couldn't survive in the climate outside.** Our efforts to provide perfect conditions for the plants have also created a potential paradise for all those creatures which see them only as lunch on a stick.

**Above left & right:** White tree frogs in the Humid Tropics Biome.
**Left:** Praying mantis.

# The loss of some lovely plants was a bitter lesson, but better then than later in the biomes.

**Above:** Bug busting in the nursery.
**Below:** Biological control is achieved by releasing beneficial insects.
**Right:** 'Soft chemicals' such as soaps are used as required to control pests.
**Cut out:** One of the gecko lizards introduced to control the pests in the medium and higher planting.

The mature olive, fig and citrus trees imported from Italy were riddled with nasty nematodes, tiny roundworms which could have caused difficulties if they had made it into the Warm Temperate Biome. It was a bit of a scare, but it did emphasize one of the major benefits of having the nursery; problems like this can be contained, controlled and eradicated.

There was a similar small crisis when a shipment of tropical plants arrived from Europe with an apparently clean bill of health, but were then found to have some thuggish stowaways – the caterpillars of the Sugar Cane Boring Moth. Boring by name, boring by nature.

The dull-brown moth itself is easy enough to kill with light traps or nicotine smoke. But the caterpillars burrow their way deep into the soft stems of bananas, ginger, palms and, obviously, sugar cane. That makes them very tricky to deal with. Biological weapons such as nematodes (friendly ones, this time) and caterpillar-killing bacteria were tried, but sadly some of the plants had to go on a funeral pyre.

Officials from the Department of Environment, Food and Rural Affairs have been very helpful in dealing with these problems. The loss of some lovely plants was a bitter lesson.

Some other wildlife have joined the staff, natural predators such as gecko lizards and tree frogs, to mop up not only the odd insect here on holiday but the more numerous locals, such as whitefly and red spider mite.

Peter Whitbread-Abrutat, Head of Technical Support for the Green Team, says, 'It all demonstrated that we have to be vigilant and appreciate the importance of proper procedures. As long as we are really stringent in monitoring these sorts of things, we can treat them if we catch them early – although I don't think it is possible to eliminate all risk.'

Among the pests that will beat the system are cockroaches. We don't have them yet, but we need to be on the lookout. They are not a problem for the plants; they are simply very unwelcome and extremely difficult to eradicate. There are over 3,500 species, mainly in the tropics, and they are the bane of botanical gardens worldwide. So some other wildlife have joined the staff, natural predators such as gecko lizards and tree frogs, to mop up not only the odd insect here on holiday but the more numerous locals, such as whitefly and red spider mite. But that has meant sorting out other imponderables first – how do you stop tiny geckoes scuttling to an untimely end in the air-handling units? How many do you need? Because the biomes are so big we could wind up with the world's most lovelorn lizards. Every answer at Eden seems to breed another question.

# Plants on the
# march

Ian Martin and his nursery crew spent the summer of 2000 at Watering Lane preparing to follow 'the Big Build' with 'the Big Shift'. By then, the 6,000 square metres of glasshouses and the surrounding field were packed with botanical wonders. **Apart from the mature 'show' trees for opening, and some other plants easily obtained from commercial nurseries, virtually everything was cared for in-house – winning maximum value from the £2.5 million plant budget.**

There were all those specimens from botanical gardens and genetic resource centres to be nurtured. But, more remarkably, during that 36 months the team also grew from scratch three-quarters of the fantastic collection now settled in at Bodelva – some 70,000 plants.

That's not bad, but it still needs putting in proper context. They weren't churning out pansies by the plug-tray. These plants span an incredible range: from the hardy to the most tenderly fragile, from the most nutritionally picky to the greediest, from those requiring

near-arid sands to boggy mud-bathers. Sun-worshippers and shade-lovers, creepers and climbers, annuals and perennials, tiny ground-huggers and soaring sky-embracers – all grown almost side by side.

Growing instructions on backs of seed packets were noticeable mostly by their absence. 'Sometimes it is subconscious, you do what you think is right,' says Ian. 'You just use your intuitive feel as a grower.'

The nursery team also had one of the toughest preparation briefs at Eden: to provide plants to meet the bubbling demands of wishful design thinking, which itself was constantly being revised. Cuttings-edge stuff, you might say.

'There have been frustrations, because we couldn't plan around a comprehensive and final list,' says Ian. 'So it was never a very tidy arrangement, but I think we can feel some satisfaction in producing as many as possible of the plants that make Eden special.'

In the late spring of 2000 many of the Warm Temperate plants had been moved outside, to allow more space for production and development of Humid Tropics specimens. That helped, but it set a tight and finite deadline. Those hothouse plants had to be heading out and into the biome, so the Mediterranean plants could come in from the cold (and wet) before the first risk of frost in the autumn. Finally, the wagons rolled. By mid-November, planting out in the Humid Tropics Biome was in full swing, and Ian felt able to take his first weekend off since February. Over 10,000 plants had gone, and he waved many of them off with a sense of relief.

# Over 10,000 plants had gone, and he waved many of them off with a sense of relief.

More than ten species, including bulou and *Gmelina Arborea*, an Asian timber tree, had to be chopped right back twice to contain them in the confines of the nursery. Growing big plants in pots leaves little room for error. 'Some of those plants had been in here for two years and more – you are on a constant knife-edge with the watering, and the fertilizing.'

Despite the removals, the nursery always seemed to be full. If anything, the pace of propagation had quickened, to meet the final requirements of the design team. Throughout the winter of 2000 2001 hundreds of cuttings were grown on to fill gaps on the steep slopes of the Humid Tropics Biome, like *Monstera deliciosa*, the Swiss Cheese plant, which would sprawl and cling on with a minimum of soil. Spring meant thousands of annual seeds to germinate for the Warm Temperate Biome.

Eventually the gaps at the nursery grew, as the ground at Bodelva filled. With Eden now open, the botanical attention naturally switched to the pit, but Watering Lane will remain a hub of backroom activity. Surplus plants will always be kept in stock, because some of the exhibits will change on a seasonal basis to keep them fresh and exciting.

Ian adds: 'There'll be the need to produce plants for education purposes, which could be anything. The education team have asked us to grow cotton plants, peppers, bananas; there'll be things we haven't even thought of yet. There'll also be a certain amount of replacement planting as we continue to track down better examples of some things. We won't be under the same pressure as we were in the year leading up to opening day – but I don't think we'll ever be sitting around wondering what to do.'

37

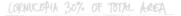

# Planting Out I:
# The Humid Tropics

On Wednesday 25 September 2000, the first palm – a *Phoenix reclinata* – was lowered carefully by crane into position in the Humid Tropics Biome.

Over the following days it rained trees as more than 250 big specimens dropped into their places on curator Robin Lock's 'painting by numbers' planting plan. This wasn't the first planting at Eden. A few weeks before, all the staff gathered for the communal planting of fifty oaks in, appropriately, the Wild Cornwall exhibit outside. That was a great bonding affair, and a proper nod to the dedication of everyone who'd played an active part in the big adventure so far. But this was something to savour. Here, now, the twin elements of that first beery idea – 'let's build the world's biggest greenhouse, and put a rainforest in it' – finally converged.

Using the crane was nerve-wracking, as the huge arm swung perilously close to the fragile foil pillows of the biome. But a fork-lift truck could not be used for fear of damaging the complex underground irrigation system, and manoeuvring upright trees like the 15-metre-high Kapok tree (*Ceiba petandra*) or the 3.5-tonne *Attalea maripa* would have been bruising for both the plants and people involved. We were too short-staffed to have anybody off with a hernia, because the real work was only just beginning.

The Humid Tropics Biome is the big draw among the Eden showcases. Not just because of the fantastic landscaping, the promise of 50-metre rainforest teaks or the diversity of plants, but also because of the extraordinary changes that will unfold along the way. In the wild, when an old tree crashes to the ground, opening a tiny chink in the canopy, that flash sparks a ruthless race as plants sprout and shoot for the light; it's the survival of the fastest. The newly planted Humid Tropics Biome was a four-acre empty clearing, with all these sprinters in their blocks.

If things were allowed to take their course, all the growth would be happening out of sight thirty metres up, with visitors stumbling around in the gloom beneath. The biomes are windows on to a world, not reality; it's going to require constant and careful attention from Robin and his team to strike the balance between feeling right and looking good. Faking the wild is a delicate job – there should be no obvious pruning here.

Peter Thoday describes it as 'covert management': 'The only way it will look natural is with a heck of a lot of human input. The dome isn't big enough to become a habitat, and it's not diverse enough to become an ecosystem – our staff will have to do all the jobs nature would normally do. They have to be the insect scavengers and break down the organic matter by carting it off to the compost heap and bringing

> In the wild, when an old tree crashes to the ground, opening a tiny chink in the canopy, that flash sparks a ruthless race as plants sprout and shoot for the light; it's the survival of the fastest.

40

it back when it is decomposed. And if we want fruits in those tropical trees, they have to take the place of the insect pollinators, going around with a camelhair brush.'

In the meantime, we are clearly not going to have the size or maturity of a natural rainforest from day one – or even year five, ten or fifteen, for that matter. But the right impression can be created by putting in those few aged monsters, creating a second layer with the saplings nurtured in the nursery, and cramming in heaps of lower in-filling plants as screening. Nobody should get too emotionally attached to any of the current big exhibits, because some of them are simply for early effect. The smaller you plant, the quicker, better and more robust trees grow. So the home-grown specimens will soon be flying past and squeezing them out. The balsas, for instance, are racing away at nearly three metres a year.

Some of the treasures trucked in from the nursery looked rough after repeated pruning to restrain them in the glasshouses. But they quickly pushed out new leaves and put on new growth. One or two offered unexpected challenges. 'When the frangipani tree came out of its pot it had virtually no roots, although it was obviously growing OK. But when we put it in the ground it fell straight over, and we had to support it with stakes and ropes,' says Robin. 'The rubber trees have almost no roots either, but they look really healthy and well. It was interesting to discover that they don't need a good root system to survive – and I hope that when people come they realize that just as they are learning, we are too. There is so much to understand about how to raise these plants in man-made conditions.'

41

Slowly, Robin, supervisor Catherine Cutler and their team of planters constructed patches of paradise: tropical South America, the oceanic islands, West Africa and Malaysia. 'We have some wonderful plants in here; I particularly like the South East Asian jeluetong rubber and chewing gum tree (*Dyera costulata*). My favourite, although it is quite boring-looking, is *Cananga odorata*, or the Ylang Ylang, used to make Chanel No. 5 perfume.'

All the plants are accurate to their geographical region. They were selected because they had a story to tell, but they are genuinely the right plants for the area. 'And when we talk about the stories,' says Robin, 'they are not only about "useful" plants, but also the social attitudes surrounding them. There are many, many examples here, like *Afzelia quansensis*, or the African mahogany tree. It's a timber tree, but there they call it "Msambafumo", or "the washing of the chief". It is the most important tree in the initiation of a new chief – he takes a bath with the leaves, which gives him his power.'

More storylines were laid in the crops exhibits, exploring the commercial bounty of the tropics. Here, says Peter Thoday, is where 'overt management' is required. 'We have to ensure we get it right, spacing the plants the correct distance apart and so on. It may only be the equivalent of a little corner of a plantation, but it is important that when a school party goes round, it is authentic.'

There is coffee – used to examine the principles and practices of Fair Trade – bananas, pineapples, bamboo, and 'fruitures', which investigates the impact our ravenous appetite for ever more exotic fruit on supermarket shelves might have both on our apple and pear industries here and on economies there. Robin, who has worked in Botswana, Malawi and Malaysia, adds: 'I hope it stimulates people not only to think and read about these things – but also to visit these places. This is a demonstration – the real stories are out there.'

'My favourite, although it is quite boring-looking, is *Cananga odorata*, or the Ylang Ylang, used to make Chanel No. 5 perfume.'

Bamboo rail
Location ①

Getting all this done was made slightly more chaotic by the fact that the builders were still in. It might have been getting nippy outside, but inside workers were stripped to the waist and sweating to complete the paths and drainage, and lay emergency lighting cables. However, while this meant dodging the odd dumper truck, it was yet another example of the hugely cooperative atmosphere that has spurred this project on from the moment the first digger scoop was dug.

It was essential that the plants had six months to settle into the soil before opening, and the construction team cheerfully accepted the aggravation of working around the planting team in the necessary tropical heat and humidity. And very useful they were too. In those first days, while the computerized climate control mechanisms were still being wired in, the temperature yo-yo'd dangerously in the alternate autumnal sun and chill. High aloft, the sky monkeys lent a hand, manually adjusting ceiling vents to try to save the plants from harm.

The temperature in the Humid Tropics Biome must be kept between 18 and 35°C, while the humidity required for all these luxuriant plants will reach 90 per cent. The lowest temperature while the planting out was happening was 10°C. It was a drastic drop and some of the plants suffered, losing their lower leaves to the cold. In the first two months the humidity was too low as well. 'Virtually all the plants survived – but we don't want to repeat the experience,' says Robin.

# Setting climate
# control

**The Humid Tropics Biome is the biggest conservatory on earth.** The temperature and humidity inside is regulated by juggling air-handling units blasting hot air, fine water-misters high up, and the vents at the top and bottom of the biomes.

Simple enough so far; these tools are universally used. But if this worked like a normal glasshouse, it would be a disaster. The greatest challenge is not keeping the biome warm – it is preventing it from becoming unbearable for visitors.

When you go into the Palm House at Kew and climb the spiral staircase, you can feel the temperature rise dramatically. That's going up about four metres. The pathways in the Humid Tropics Biome rise many times higher; if the same thing happened here, we'd probably be vaporizing visitors. But this biome contains such a huge volume of air that it has different physics, a different behaviour from any greenhouse ever built before. You can't bend the rules about heat rising, but within this sort of space you can make them work for you.

The vents in the roof are designed to have the same effect as an efficient chimney, sucking up hot air. What doesn't escape meets the moisture from the misters at the top, which absorbs the heat and starts to fall, creating a massive cycle of air circulation rolling through the biome.

# You can't bend the rules about heat rising, but within this sort of space you can make them work for you. The vents in the roof are designed to have the same effect as an efficient chimney, sucking up hot air.

This has all been carefully calculated by the engineers. It has not been attempted before. At this point it's looking great, so there's another quick sigh of relief, and we're on to the next challenge.

That'll be the one facing the staff handling the climate-control systems. They may all be computer-operated (with manual back-ups in case of crashes when the service engineer is out of town), but that will only help the team make sense of what's going on – they'll have to make the judgment on which combinations give the best response, when to lower the temperature, when to turn on a tropical mist and so on.

There's a further imponderable; the plants themselves. The condensation given off by this mass of feeding and transpiring vegetation will increase dramatically as they grow, which will have its own effect on the climate. While we have a good theoretical idea of what will happen, reality has a habit of being unpredictable. Living with all of this is going to be not so much a learning curve as a race to keep up with events.

**Above:** Setting up the climate control and automated misting in the Humid Tropics Biome.
**Below:** Temperature testing.
**Right:** Air handling units help circulate the air in the biomes.

# Planting Out II:
# The Warm Temperate Zone

The Humid Tropics Biome may be the icon of Eden – the 'jungle in a bubble' that first defined the Project – but the Warm Temperate Biome presents the greater planting challenge. Next door, superficially, it's a case of set the controls for the heart of the sauna, stick them in the ground the right way up, stand back, and watch them race into space.

**Above:** A 'Buddha's hand' in the Warm Temperate Biome.

Here in the Warm Temperate Biome, curator Tom Keay and his team are creating subtler plantscapes of slow-ageing and seasonal change. In contrast to the perpetual luxuriant greenery of the Humid Tropics, they will be encouraging crop cycles and swathes of vibrant flowering bulbs and annuals to bloom, while simultaneously pegging back wiry survivors – which will require deft juggling of warmth and water.

Here lies the cradle of civilization around the Mediterranean, with its citrus, olives, lavenders, sage, thyme and vines; the rich variety of the Fynbos, found on the Western Cape of South Africa, where Proteas, Restios and Ericas grow, accompanied by the Aloe species and other succulents from hot scree slopes; drifts of colourful Californian annuals

Think annuals and grasses; think air-borne seeds. If this was an exhibition of wild Britain under glass, you might soon wind up with a biome full of dandelions.

– poppies, Penstemon species and lupins – grow amongst the Chaparral shrubs such as *Ceanothus* and *Arctostaphylos* species; a cornucopia of vines, fruits, vegetables, pulses and grains.

The concept is of distinct, defined, areas which demonstrate how plants have adapted to habitats, and how mankind in turn has adapted the plants for his own use. But instead of being separated by thousands of miles, these areas are only metres apart. And that leads to one of the less obvious management headaches. Think annuals and grasses; think air-borne seeds. If this was an exhibition of wild Britain under glass, you might soon wind up with a biome full of dandelions. They'll face the same battle to prevent California invading the Med.

Biome supervisor Glen Leishman says, 'We want to achieve an ecologically accurate look for these areas – but it has had to be tweaked a little, by planting these things in specific places where we can monitor and control them. Otherwise we are going to be spending all our time weeding.'

More tweaking has been necessary to push the seed-packet of seasonal display. The team is trying to ensure a succession of new flowering, sweeping around the Warm Temperate Biome for as long as possible through the year. The biome will be perfect for the plants during the summer months – it is well sited for high light levels, and has plenty of ventilation. But the gardeners will have to be on their toes in the winter. They have to bring the temperature down – many of these plants need a dormant season. But the moist Cornish air means that there is a real danger of them damping-off.

To add to the confusion, the Warm Temperate Biome not only matches climatic regions, it is mixing hemispheres. Some of the South African bulbs can apparently suffer a sort of permanent jet lag, insisting on flowering in our autumn because that would be their spring.

'It is all quite complex,' says Tom Keay. 'So many things need slightly different treatment, and I'm sure we are not going to get it right all the time, because a lot of this has never been attempted before – but that's part of the excitement.'

Ironically, while the biomes have been designed to provide the optimum conditions for plants to flourish, many, like the sages and thymes, live starved and rough in their native state. For authenticity, the Green Team has to be cruel to be kind. Tom says, 'People are going to walk in and see an old scruffy sage bush – but that is the look we want to recreate.

'Lush growth here would be ridiculous. Some of the things imported from Italy were potted up in the nursery and became very green and healthy. I looked at them and thought, well, OK – enjoy it for now, but that's not what I want. And then there were some lovely old Cistus that had gone all woody and looked potbound, really struggling – I thought, yes, we've got to keep those, because that is exactly how it really is.

'Basically, we are going to have to grow them hard, and stress them out. We've got the soil right, but we're finding out the rest as we go. For instance, high winds have a dramatic impact on the way some of these plants develop. We haven't got that here, so we have to devise ways of achieving that effect, which might mean cutting some of them back quite severely to keep them down.'

Cut out entirely from the display are, sadly, some of the mature trees sought out to add instant age – the Warm Temperate Biome collection was the hardest hit by the problems with imported pests.

'That was heartbreaking,' says Tom. 'I had other wonderful specimens lined up ready to bring over, like some more citrus, and lovely gnarled old pomegranate trees, but it just wasn't worth the risk, or the trouble of having to clean them all. The trees themselves were obviously growing quite happily with those nematodes there, but there are a lot of other plants in the biomes that could have been dramatically affected.'

Fortunately, the scrubby and low-growing nature of these regions meant that redesigning to plug the gaps was more a matter of amending wish-lists than averting disaster – all these trees and many more had been propagated at Watering Lane.

'It is fantastic, giving a real sense of the places; very colourful, with the big spreads of Californian plants, and a great sensory experience with the tremendous smell from the Mediterranean herbs,' says Tom. 'Because a lot of the material is annual and herbaceous stuff, I think that after just one growing season the biome is looking pretty established.'

53

'Basically, we are going to have to grow them hard, and stress them out.'

# Planting Out III: The **Temperate** Zone

Landscape architect Dominic Cole drew on his affection for the quilt-like patchwork of the quintessential British allotment in designing it. It has been likened to a stylized satellite hurricane picture: the arena at the calm eye of the storm, an exciting whirl of busy stories of how man has interfered with plants to create crops moving up the terrace blades, thinning to a wisp of wild places on the perimeter showing the marriage of land use and conservation.

Clearly, through this keyhole lies a place of many interpretations. Compared with the samba of the Tropics, or flamenco of the Latin quarter, the great outdoors we're representing at Eden could be dismissed as a dowdy sibling hopping to the Morris dance beat a bit of a wallflower. That would be a big mistake.

The Temperate Landscape (and Morris dancing, we hasten to add) is equally alluring; familiarity should not blind visitors to its attractions and many hidden talents. Everything that is in those two biomes will be out here, in triplicate, if taking a little longer to mature. If you've ever wanted for food, clothes, shelter, medicine, rope – look no further. This is where Eden's story – and a major chunk of our educational ambition – comes in, and this is where we really feel compelled to press home the messages.

The design collaboration of Dominic Cole and Helen Rosevear had first to be delivered up, however, and it was a messy business; planting started during the deluges of the wettest autumn on record

Overnight, rain run-off repeatedly carved canyons into the exposed slopes. We quickly discovered that we hadn't managed to cap all the myriad springs that once peppered the site; usually after the water had built up behind an earth bank until it flopped as lumpy mud custard on to the path below.

Tom Keay, who is also Curator of this outside area, says, 'It was a logistical nightmare, and grim going for the gardeners, but they were remarkably cheerful and keen. I kept telling them they would only have to do this once – when the plants are in, the problem is sorted, because their roots stabilize the slopes.'

This 'biome' will take longer than the others to settle down and take shape, but visitors will appreciate that from their experience with their own gardens. Given a year to get established, it will look really impressive, with big slabs of planting here and there, and with all the colours; the perfect setting for the biomes.

For the structure planting, which provides the settings for the exhibit jewels, Tom and his team have taken advantage of Cornwall's mild maritime climate and the sheltered site to push the boundaries of what can be brought to bloom. Perhaps people have one or two of them as precious specimens in their own gardens – well, this is wide-screen Cinemascope planting, showing what five hundred or more look like together, swathes of tender Bottlebrush and ornamental *Grevillea*, great belts of *Agapanthus*, *Pittosporum* and Myrtle.

An exotic plot will tiptoe to the very edge of hardiness, with cacti and Agaves. Tom says, 'A lot of visitors will not be particularly interested in plants, but others will be really keen gardeners. So we have that sort of fun and unusual thing to intrigue them. You can never underestimate the knowledge and expertise of the amateur gardener – because many specialize in particular species or varieties, they often know more about what I'm growing than I do. That's why this all has to be pitched at different levels. It can't be bland, we have to cover wide degrees of interest, so people can learn something or see something that excites them.'

Out on the edges at the top of the slopes are two of the early conservation projects already underway at Eden. There's the Chilean rainforest, and Wild Cornwall, which also presents a perfect example of the kind of partnership Eden was in part founded to foster – here with Plantlife, the national conservation charity, and English Nature, the government conservation agency. Lowland heath is one of the most endangered habitats in Europe. Cornwall is one of its last strongholds, and English Nature is currently involved in a programme to restore vast areas of heathland on china clay waste.

On their behalf, Eden is demonstrating three different techniques.

Well, this is wide-screen Cinemascope planting, showing what five hundred or more look like together, swathes of tender Bottle-brush and ornamental Grevillea, great belts of Agapanthus, Pittosporum and Myrtle.

There is one area of 'here's some we prepared earlier' turfs taken from established heathland; another where soil from existing heathland has been spread to see what germinates and grows; and a third, where seed collected in the wild has been mixed with water and green waste, and then 'spray-planted' - the same hydro-seeding method used to grass the banks around the pit.

It will produce tangible experience, which can then be applied back out there in the real world. Tom Keay says, 'We are particularly pleased to have that heathland as a shop window, to encourage people to go out and explore the wild landscape in Cornwall, and to appreciate that practical, positive action is possible for restoring these endangered areas.'

It doesn't scream for attention in the in-your-face fashion of a tropical orchid display, however. During the planning for the temperate biome, interpretation has had to be really imaginative so as to pull the eyes and the feet around.

'A lot of these plants outside are really important,' Tom says. 'Some of them are wonderful in flower, like the lavender or sunflowers. But others, like some of the plants for paper or plants for fuel, are not visually that interesting. They need more work to convey their importance, to point out that this really is a great story, that it could help boost Cornish agriculture, or whatever.'

So great effort is being applied to turning plants that might have seemed hardly worth a glance into stop, stare and wonder features; a powerful blend of horticulture, art and science.

# Taking Eden into the Future

Just two and a half years separated the day in October 1998 when the first excavator rumbled into the sterile, empty moonscape of a china clay quarry, and the full public opening of these unique biomes greened with plantlife and churning with activity. Everything so far has been done at such a breathless pace, and virtually all effort during that time has been concentrated on simply making the place fit to entertain guests. It has been difficult to think far beyond that.

Of course, Eden isn't leaping fully formed into the world; it is telling a story of evolution, and it is evolving and developing itself. There is still a fair bit of work to do around the site. Even so, the Eden Project is up and running, and the sheer number of visitors suggests that we're on the right track.

We were always confident that we could build something that would capture the imagination. Are we confident about spending £80 million and more? Are we confident everything will work? It would be false to say we have blind faith. We have the skills and the reasonable view that with a following wind it will – but we were only capable of imagining it working in a much smaller context. Because no one has ever built anything like this before.

What happens next?
Keep coming to find out.

## Watch us grow!

# Photo credits

Printed on paper from a managed, sustainable forest using a process that is totally chlorine free.